THE MATT MERTON
MYSTERIES

THE END: PART 2

D0417135

Paul Blum

RISING★STARS

nasen

NASEN House, 4/5 Amber Business Village, Amber Close,
Amington, Tamworth, Staffordshire B77 4RP

Rising Stars UK Ltd.
7 Hatchers Mews, Bermondsey Street, London SE1 3GS
www.risingstars-uk.com

Text © Rising Stars UK Ltd.
The right of Paul Blum to be identified as the author of this work has
been asserted by him in accordance with the Copyright, Design and
Patents Act, 1988.

Published 2010
Reprinted 2013

Cover design: pentacorbig
Illustrator: Chris King, Illustration Ltd
Photos: Alamy
Text design and typesetting: pentacorbig/Clive Sutherland
Publisher: Gill Budgell
Editorial consultants: Lorraine Petersen and Dee Reid

British Library Cataloguing in Publication Data.
A CIP record for this book is available from the British Library.

ISBN: 978-1-84680-801-2

Printed by Craft Print International Limited, Singapore

THE MATT MERTON MYSTERIES

CONTENTS

THE CRASH

The Crash happened in 2021. Alien
spaceships crash-landed on Earth.
Now the aliens rule the world. They
have changed shape so they look
like people. People call the aliens The
Enemy. Since The Crash, people are
afraid. They don't know who is an
Enemy and who is a friend.

An organisation called The Firm keeps
order on the streets. The Firm keeps
people safe from Enemy attacks – or
do they?

People are going missing and the Earth
is becoming colder and darker all the
time. A new ice age is coming ...

ABOUT MATT MERTON

Matt Merton works for The Firm. He often works with **Dexter**. Their job is to find and kill The Enemy. They use Truth Sticks to do this.

But Matt has problems. He has lost some of his memory and cannot answer some big questions.

Where has **Jane**, his girlfriend, gone?

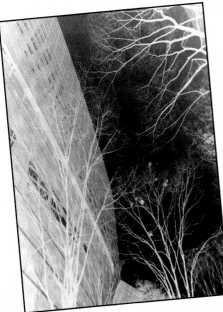

How did he get his job with **The Firm**?

Matt thinks The Firm is on the side of good. But he is not sure …

CHAPTER 1

At dawn, Matt, Jane and Sam went to Route 6. The sky was dark. It was snowing. Matt shivered from both cold and fear. A new ice age was coming and they were going to try to stop it.

'It's so cold,' said Matt.

'In a few hours, we'll see the Sun again,' said Sam.

Trucks drove past them into Route 6. They were full of prisoners. Matt could see that they had been beaten. He knew none of these people had done bad things. Matt had worked for The Firm. He had handed people over to Route 6. He felt so bad.

Sam squeezed Matt's arm. He knew what Matt was thinking and tried to cheer him up.

'We'll stop them,' he said. 'The aliens won't freeze us out. After today, they will need more than a pair of sunglasses to live on this planet.'

Jane smiled. 'In a few hours, we'll all need sunglasses,' she said, as a truck drove past. 'Let's go!'

As the trucks went into Route 6 they slowed down. Jane, Matt and Sam jumped onto the back of one of the trucks. The snow blew in their faces as the truck picked up speed. But they got past the alien guard without being seen. They were inside Route 6.

When the truck stopped, they got off and hid in the shadows.

'This is mad,' said Sam. 'They'll find us and kill us.'

'It's the only way to get rid of the aliens,' said Jane.

'Trust me, Sam,' said Matt. 'I'm not ready to die. I've got too many things to put right.' Matt looked at Jane. He took her hand.

'You're trained for this saving the world stuff,' said Sam. 'And you've got each other. I've got nobody to stop me being frightened.'

Matt put his hand on Sam's shoulder. 'We need you, Sam,' Matt smiled. 'And I need you to be alive to make me a coffee when this is all over!'

CHAPTER 2

There was no sound inside Route 6. Everyone sat at a computer. The computers kept up a shield that blocked the Sun. If the Sun came out, the aliens would die from the light and heat.

'Why are they all so quiet?' asked Matt.

'Speaking is forbidden,' said Jane. 'They have to watch out for any changes in the way that the Sun's rays hit Earth. They have to shut out the heat and light for long enough to start a new ice age. They are getting very close to doing that. We don't have much time.'

'We must find the main computer and shut it down,' said Matt.

Then an alien saw them.

'I don't think he's too happy about us breaking the rules on talking,' said Jane.

'Do you think he'll leave us alone if we just stop talking and sit down?' Sam said.

'I think it's too late for that,' Matt replied. 'He looks very angry and so do his friends.'

More aliens entered the room. The one nearest to them roared like a lion. Its eyes were gleaming. Its teeth were sharp. It had three very large fingers on each hand. It grabbed Sam around the neck. Matt moved quickly. He knew he had only seconds to save all their lives.

Matt snapped his Truth Stick in half. The shrill noise of the broken Truth Stick panicked the aliens. They started to shake. They could not move.

'They don't like heat and they don't like high-pitched noises either,' said Matt. 'I found that out at The Firm. I said working there would come in handy.'

The sound of the Truth Stick made the prisoners snap out of their silent state. They stopped working at the computers. At once, the shield started to lose power. The Sun's rays would break through any minute.

Then the prisoners attacked the aliens. They ran at them and fought them with their bare hands. The fight for freedom had started.

CHAPTER 3

Matt, Jane and Sam ran upstairs to the main computer room. It was very dark. The alien leader sat at the computer. Its eyes glowed.

'Matt Merton, I've been waiting for you,' it said. 'I knew you would bring Jane to me in the end. Dexter failed. You did not. We trained you well.'

The door slammed behind them.

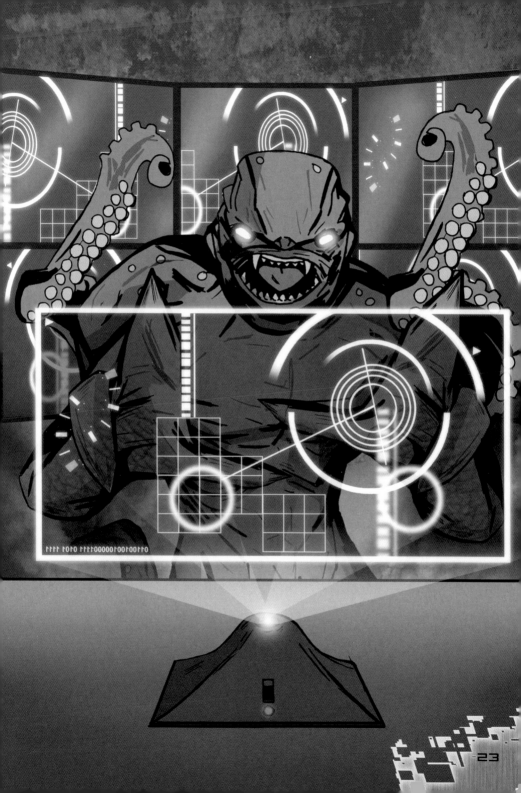

'It's over,' said Matt. 'We're taking our planet back.'

'I should have killed you before,' said the alien. 'But I will kill you now.'

Matt took out another Truth Stick. He held it up to the alien leader. 'Let's see what truth you will tell,' he said with a smile on his face.

'I will not play your games,' said the alien leader. 'I made the Truth Sticks. I gave them to The Firm. When you were in The Firm you followed my orders. You killed The Enemy. You will kill for me again.'

'Not now I know who the real enemy is,' Matt shouted.

'You will obey me!' replied the alien leader. Its many arms and legs reached for Jane and Sam. They tried to get out of the way but the alien was too fast and too strong. It had them trapped.

But at that moment, Matt smashed the main computer. There was a flash of light.

'It looks like I don't obey you anymore,' said Matt. 'It's too late to stop us. The shield is coming down. It's over!'

A small ray of sunshine hit the window. The
alien leader tried to grab Matt but it had started
to burn. Its arms and legs started to shake
and twitch. It dropped Jane and Sam. 'No!' he
shouted. 'You are weak. I rule this planet. The ice
age is coming.'

But Matt kept on smashing the computer. 'It is not
coming,' he said. 'You're not going to destroy my
world. Not now, not ever!'

Outside the light grew brighter. The computers had stopped and the shield was coming down.

The Sun was back at last. It began to warm the Earth. The snow started to melt. The sky grew lighter and lighter.

The alien leader tried to run into the shadows, but the light was everywhere. Smoke came off its skin. It was on fire. There was nothing it could do to stop the Sun.

Bit by bit the alien started melting. Its face caved in and its body sagged. It gave one last scream of pain.

33

Then it was gone.

'Look!' said Sam. 'All the aliens are dying.'

They watched as Route 6 filled up with the strange creatures. They were trying to escape but there was nowhere for them to go. The aliens were melting before their eyes.

Sam, Jane and Matt looked out over the city. They could not believe their eyes.

'We really did it,' said Matt. 'It's all over.'

Jane smiled. 'You did it, Matt. You saved the world.'

'You're a hero,' grinned Sam as he hugged Matt.

'I couldn't have done it on my own,' said Matt, looking at Sam and Jane. 'It was a team effort.'

CHAPTER 4

Four months later, Matt and Jane were sitting outside Sam's new cafe.

'Can I have a coffee, Sam? Extra hot with an extra shot,' said Jane.

'I've heard that before,' said Sam, smiling.

'We're going on holiday next week,' said Matt.

'Are you going skiing?' joked Sam. 'You must be missing the snow.'

'No way,' said Matt. 'We're going surfing!'

'It's a celebration really,' said Jane. She was wearing a sparkling diamond ring.

Sam was pleased that Matt and Jane were getting married. 'That's great news. I was bored with seeing Matt sitting in a dark corner with his head in his hands ...'

'... Trying to work out what had gone wrong with my life,' said Matt. 'Everything is sorted out now.'

He looked at Jane and everybody smiled.

'Look at the blossom on those trees, Sam,' said Matt. 'It's another lovely day.'

'Spring is here again,' said Jane.

The Sun was out. The sky was blue. The aliens had gone and the world could live again. It really was the start of something new.

QUIZ

1. What was in the trucks entering Route 6?

2. What did Sam say the aliens might soon need to wear?

3. What does Matt say to stop Sam feeling scared?

4. What is forbidden in Route 6?

5. How did the prisoners fight back against the aliens?

6. Who is guarding the main computer room?

7. What did the alien leader give to The Firm?

8. What happens to the aliens as the Sun comes back?

9. What is Jane wearing at the end of the story?

10. What season is it four months after the aliens were beaten?

GLOSSARY

forbidden – not allowed

gleaming – shine brightly

guard – someone who watches over people or a place

panicked – shocked and confused

prisoner – person being held against their will

silent state – not making a sound

ANSWERS

1. Prisoners

2. Sunglasses

3. That he needs Sam to make a coffee for him after they have beaten the aliens

4. Speaking

5. They attack them with their bare hands

6. The alien leader

7. Truth Sticks

8. They burn and melt away

9. A diamond ring

10. Spring

CASE FILE

AUTHOR NAME
Paul Blum

JOB
Teacher

LAST KNOWN LOCATION
London, England

NOTES

Before The Crash taught in London schools. Author of *The Extraordinary Files* and *Shadows*. Believed to be in hiding from The Firm. Wanted for questioning. Seems to know more about the new ice age than he should ...

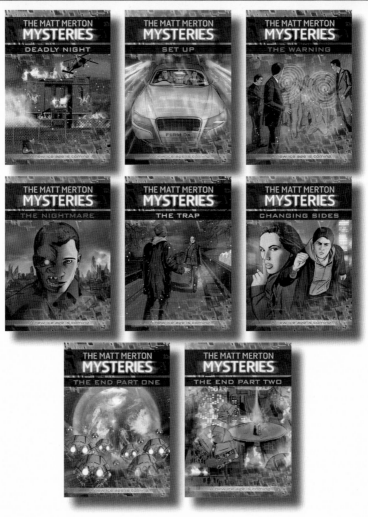